Piano Theory Workbook

GW00836211

Authors
**Barbara Kreader, Fred Kern, Phillip Keveren,
Mona Rejino, Karen Harrington**

Director, Educational Keyboard Publications
Margaret Otwell

Editors
Carol Klose, Rodney Kendall

Illustrator
Fred Bell

FOREWORD

The **Piano Theory Workbooks** present theory writing assignments that coordinate page-by-page with the **Piano Lessons** books in the **Hal Leonard Student Piano Library**.

Spike, Party Cat and friends guide the student through fun and creative activities that introduce the language of music and its symbols for sound, silence and rhythm. Ear training exercises and basic theory help students learn to write and play the music they are learning as well as the music they create themselves.

Best wishes,

Barbara Kreader   Fred Kern   Phillip Keveren

Mona Rejino   Karen Harrington

ISBN 978-0-7935-8618-9

7777 W. BLUEMOUND RD. P.O. BOX 13819 MILWAUKEE, WI 53213

Visit Hal Leonard Online at
www.halleonard.com

Feel the Beat!

Sit quietly and listen to your heartbeat.
Feel how it beats with a steady pulse.

1. Circle the things that have a steady beat.

2. Draw a picture of something that makes a steady, ticking sound.

High or Low?

Your teacher will play four musical examples.
Circle the picture in each box that matches the sound of the music – high or low.

1.

2.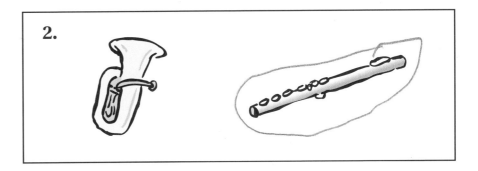

3.

4.

Teacher's Examples on pg. 48

Use with Lesson Book 1, pg. 5

Finger Numbers

Trace your hands and write the correct number on each finger.

Left Hand

Right Hand

Colour your 1st fingers blue.   Colour your 2nd fingers yellow.
Colour your 4th fingers red.   Colour your 5th fingers green.

Colour your 3rd fingers orange.

Number That Finger!

Which fingers are wearing the rings?
Write the correct finger number in each box.

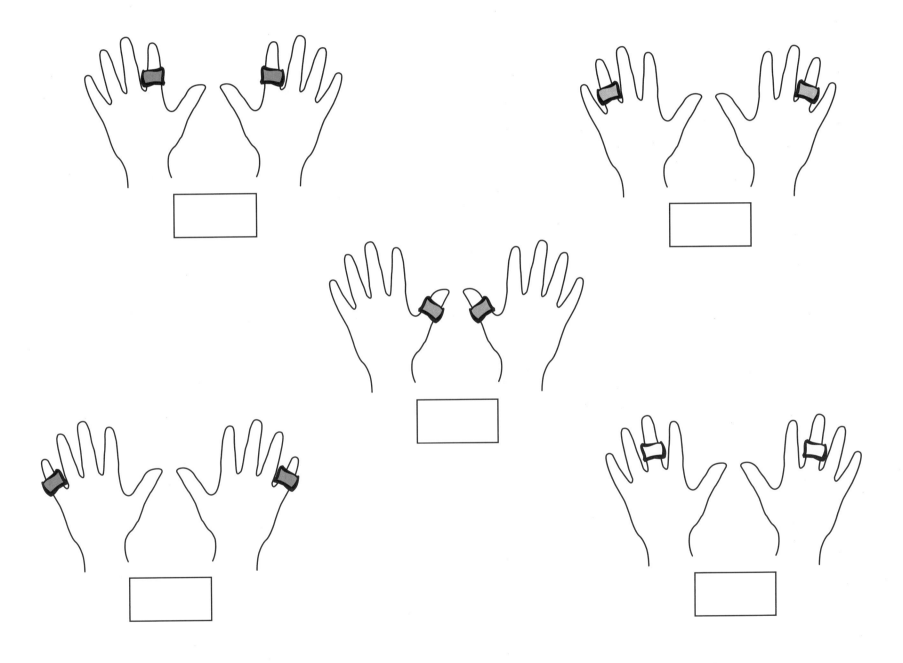

Circle each set of two blackbirds.

Two Black Keys

Colour each set of two black keys.

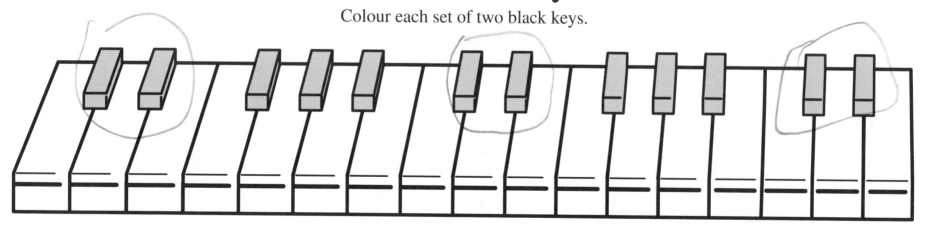

On the piano: Play two black keys way down low.
Play two black keys way up high.

Circle each set of three blackbirds.

Three Black Keys

Colour each set of three black keys.

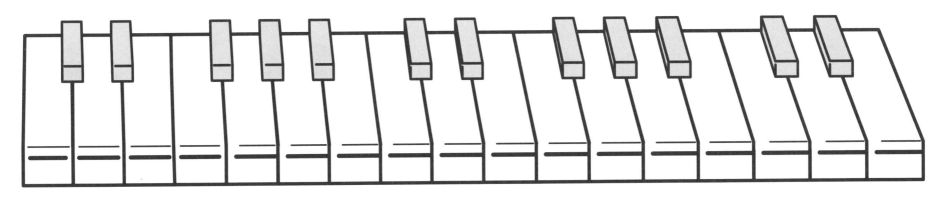

On the piano: Play three black keys way down low.
Play three black keys way up high.

Party Cat's Bubbles

Party Cat loves to make bubbles.
Trace and colour each one.

Notes

Notes are pictures of sound.

Turn Party Cat's bubbles into notes.
Trace and colour each one.

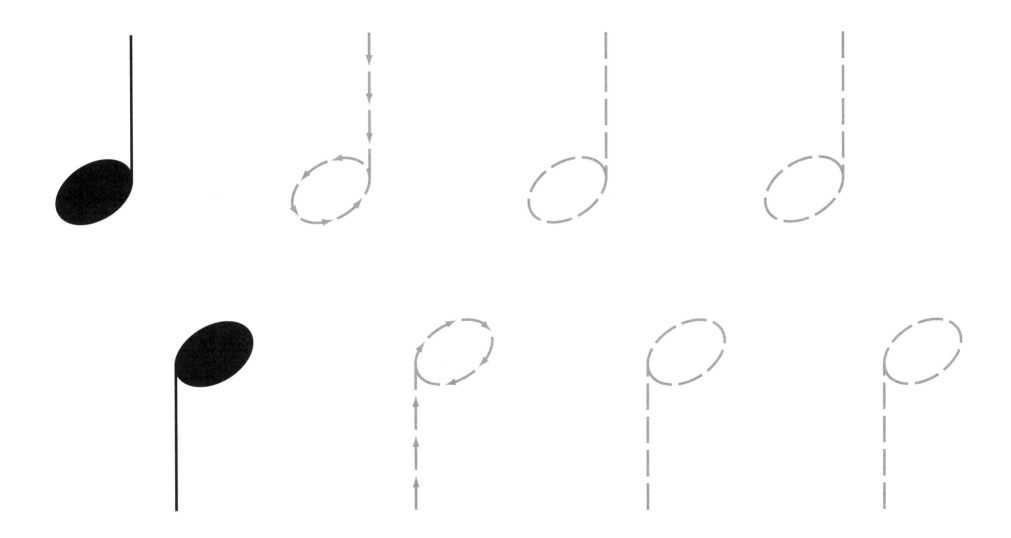

Use with Lesson Book 1, pg. 12

Left Hand

Left or Right?

Write "L.H." in the left hands and "R.H." in the right hands.

Right Hand

Which Hand Plays?

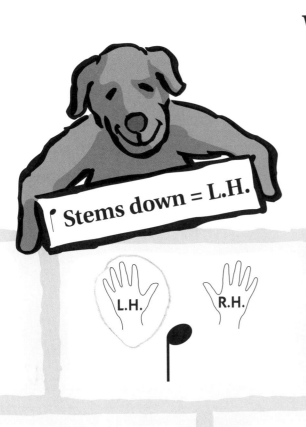

Circle the hand that plays each note.

Draw the stem to match each hand.

L.H.

R.H.

L.H.

R.H.

L.H.

Use with Lesson Book 1, pg. 14

Drawing Rests

shhh

A rest is a picture of silence.

CROTCHET RESTS

Rest for one beat.

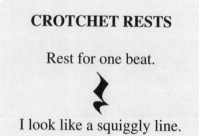

I look like a squiggly line.

MINIM RESTS

Rest for two beats.

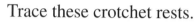

I look like a hat.

Trace these crotchet rests.

Trace these minim rests.

Your teacher will tap or play one of the rhythms in each box.
1. Circle the rhythm you hear.
2. Choose one note on the piano and play the rhythm you circled.

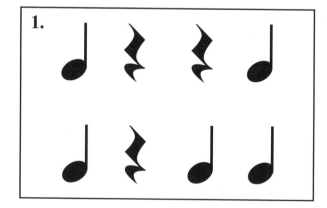

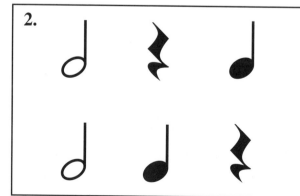

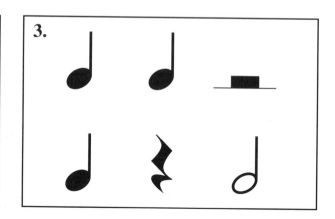

Rhythm Detective

Find the missing notes and rests!

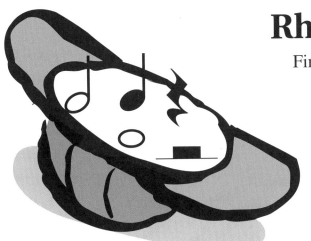

A note or rest is missing from every bar below. When completed, every bar has exactly four beats.
1. Choose a correct note or rest from the detective's hat.
2. Draw the missing note or rest in the box in each bar.

Now it's your teacher's turn to guess!
Choose a note on the piano and play one of the five rhythms keeping a steady pulse.
Ask your teacher to guess which rhythm you played.

Rhythm Composer

Each fish bowl contains the notes and rests
you will need to compose the bars below.

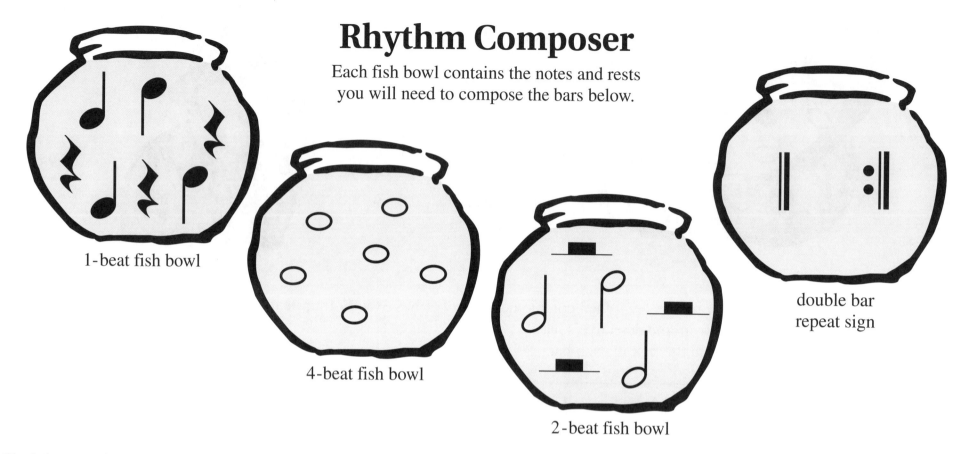

1-beat fish bowl

4-beat fish bowl

2-beat fish bowl

double bar
repeat sign

Each bar needs exactly four beats.
Choose notes or rests from each fish bowl and draw them in the bars below.

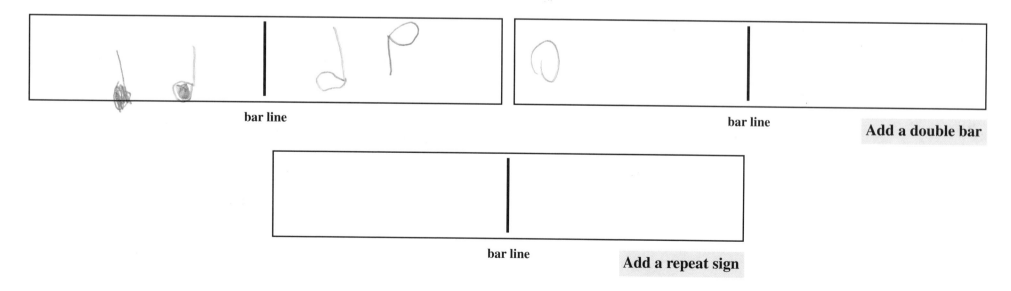

bar line

bar line

Add a double bar

bar line

Add a repeat sign

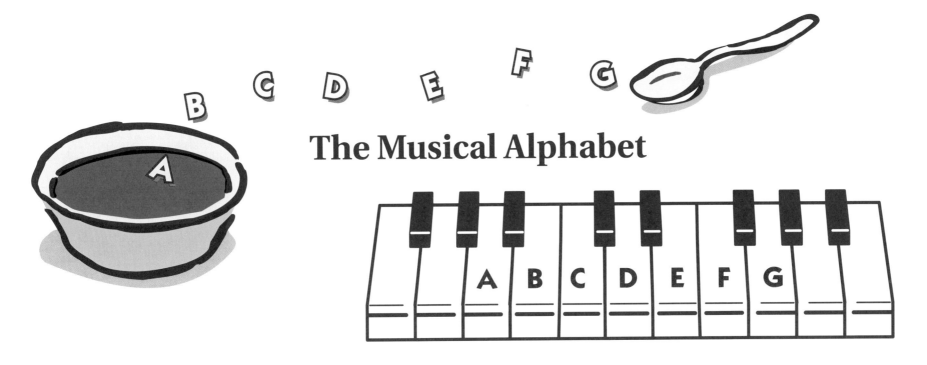

The Musical Alphabet

On each keyboard below, start with the given letter and write the musical alphabet.
The arrows will direct you to write the alphabet forwards or backwards.

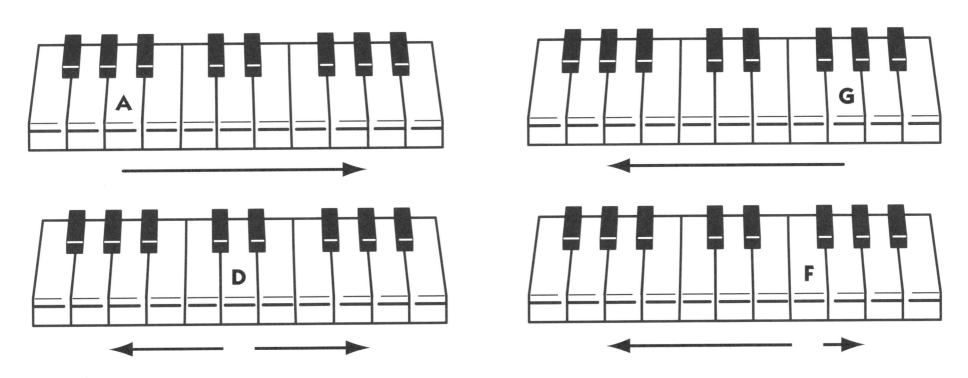

Use with Lesson Book 1, pg. 21

C D E Groups

1. Circle the sets of two black keys.
2. Write the C D E letter names on the white keys.
3. Colour the C's red, the D's blue, and the E's green.

Finding C D E
on the Keyboard

Party Cat is inviting some animal friends to his birthday party,
but he can't remember how to spell all their names.

Help him by filling in the missing letters.
1. Write the name of each outlined key in the blank below it.
2. Colour the C's red, the D's blue, and the E's green.

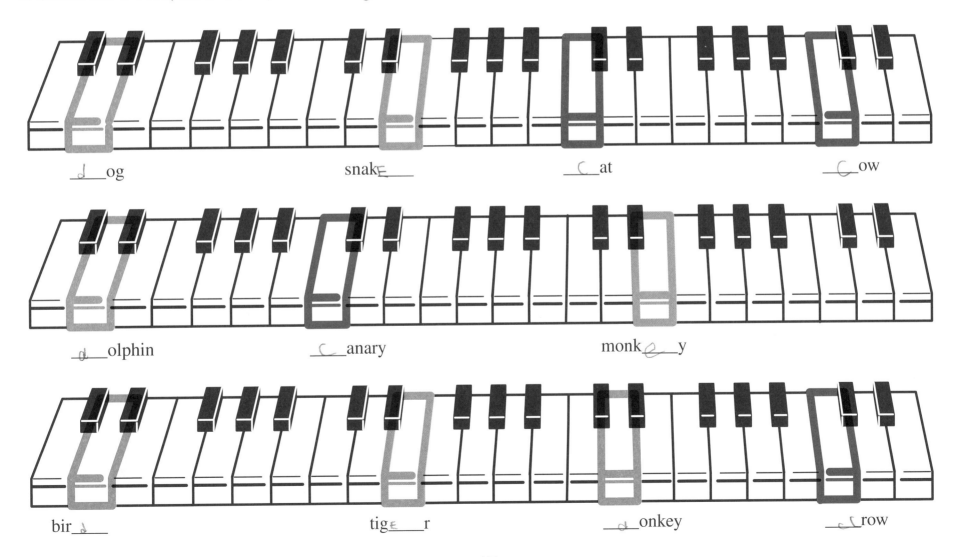

D og   snakE   Cat   Cow

D olphin   Canary   monkEy

birD   tigEr   Donkey   Crow

17

F G A B Groups

1. Circle the sets of three black keys.
2. Write the F G A B letter names on the white keys.
3. Colour the F's yellow, the G's purple, the A's orange, and the B's brown.

Finding F G A B on the Keyboard

Spike is taking a taxi to his house at the end of Keyboard Lane.
Help the taxi driver follow Spike's directions to his house.

1. Circle the sets of three black keys.

2. Drive to the first F and colour it yellow.

3. Drive to the next F and colour it yellow.

4. Drive to the next A and colour it orange.

5. Drive to the next G and colour it purple.

6. Drive to the next B and colour it brown.

7. Drive to the next G and colour it purple.

8. Drive to the next A and colour it orange.

9. Drive to the next F and colour it yellow.

10. Drive to the next B and colour it brown.

Hooray! Spike's home!

Use with Lesson Book 1, pg. 28

Naming Notes on the Keyboard

Find the coloured keys that match the coloured boxes below.
To complete this story, write the letter names
of the keys in the coloured boxes.

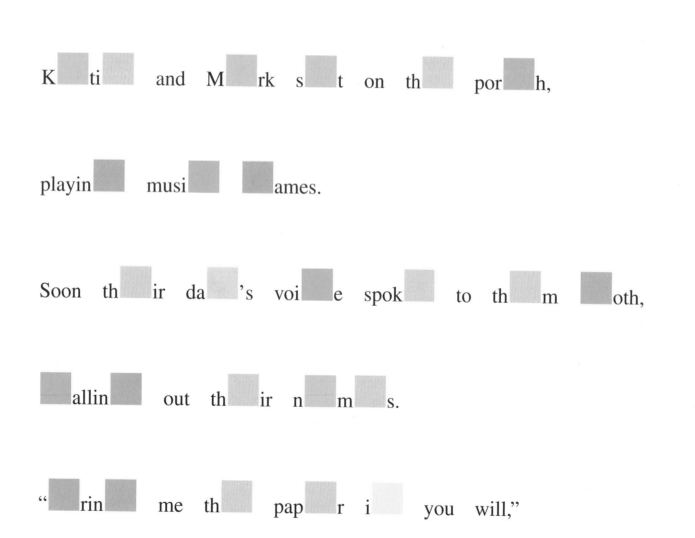

K ti and M rk s t on th por h,

playin musi ames.

Soon th ir da 's voi e spok to th m oth,

allin out th ir n m s.

" rin me th pap r i you will,"

he ___sked rom 'round the ___oor.

Y___t ___oth o the ___hil___ren, not wantin___ to stop,

pl___yed just ___ minute mor___.

When in___lly th___y inished and looke___ for th___ p___per,

no si___n o it ___ould they see,

Only ___mpty ___reen ___rass with resh mu___ ___y p___w prints,

where ___o you think it ___ould ___e?   Who took the paper?

Spike got it.

LOUD   or   *Soft?*
forte – *f*   piano – *p*

Imagine the way each picture sounds.
Write *p* for soft or *f* for loud in the box below each picture.

p

Rhythm Jam

When Old MacDonald's band began rehearsing music for its next show,
they discovered that some of the bars weren't complete.

Circle the one note or rest in the blue box
that will complete each bar.

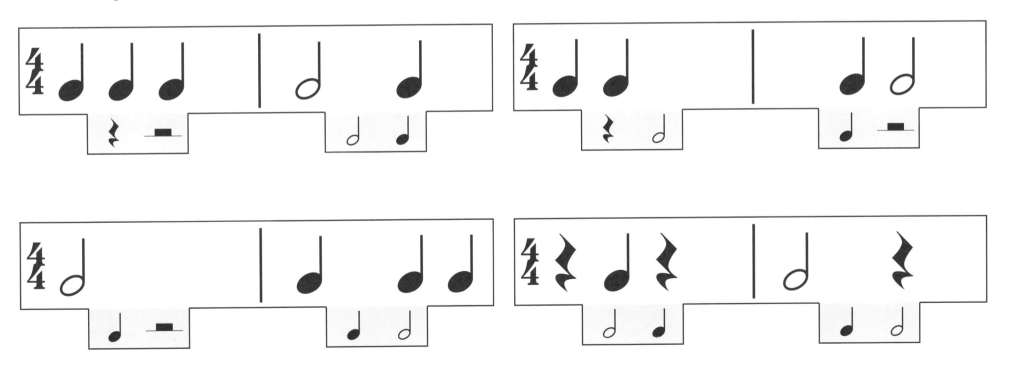

Use with Lesson Book 1, pg. 34

Step or Repeat

The pig from Old MacDonald's Band is missing
some of the note names from his favorite songs.

1. Using the arrows as guides, write the name of the
   mystery note in the blank above or below each one.
2. Play each two-bar example.

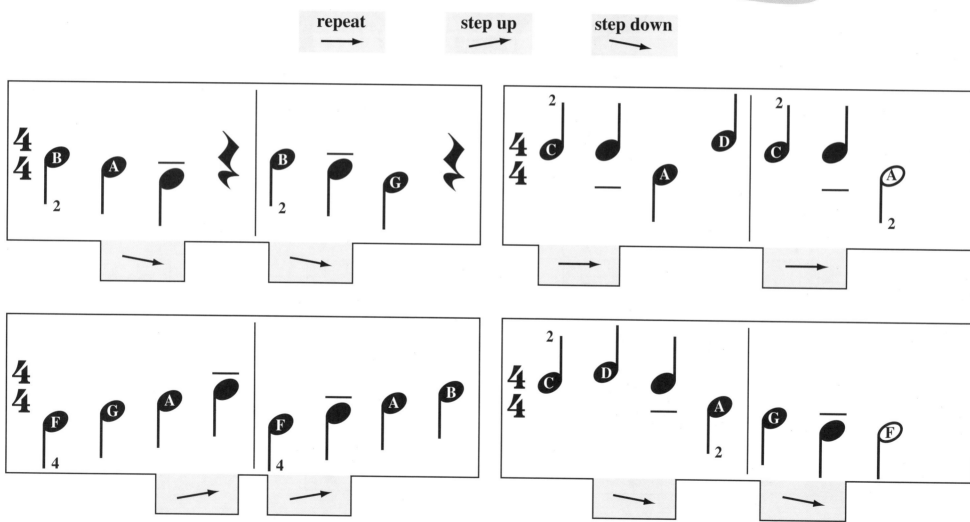

Line Note ‑o‑ or Space Note ‑o‑ ?

Come and play on the line-space jungle gym.

1. Circle each child's face.
   The circle will look like either a line note or a space note.
2. Underline the correct answer.

line note
space note

line note
space note

line note
space note

line note
space note

line note
space note

line note
space note

Notes on Lines

Party Cat likes to draw line notes.
He also likes to mix them up!

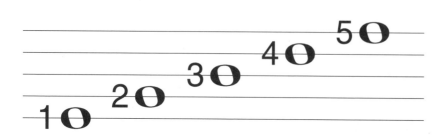

Write the correct line number in the box next to each note.

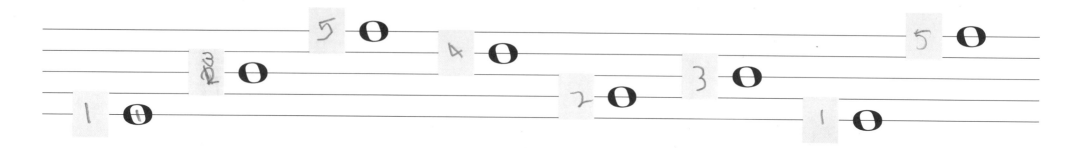

Draw a semibreve note next to each number.

Notes in Spaces

Spike likes to draw space notes,
but he wants to go outside and play.
Help him complete his work.

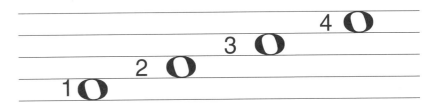

Write the correct space number in the box next to each note.

Draw a semibreve note next to each number.

Use with Lesson Book 1, pg. 36

How Notes Move

Help Party Cat decorate some balloons for his music party.

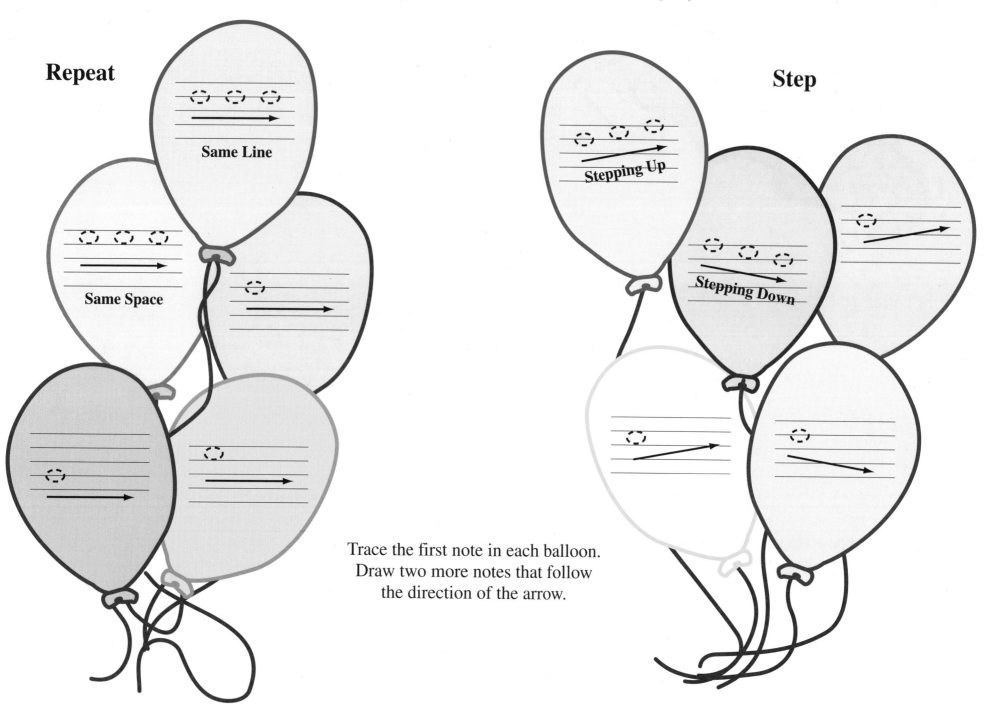

Repeat

Same Line

Same Space

Step

Stepping Up

Stepping Down

Trace the first note in each balloon.
Draw two more notes that follow
the direction of the arrow.

Up, Down, or Repeat

Your teacher will play six musical patterns.

Draw ——→ if the notes move up, ——→ if the notes move down, or ——→ if the notes repeat.

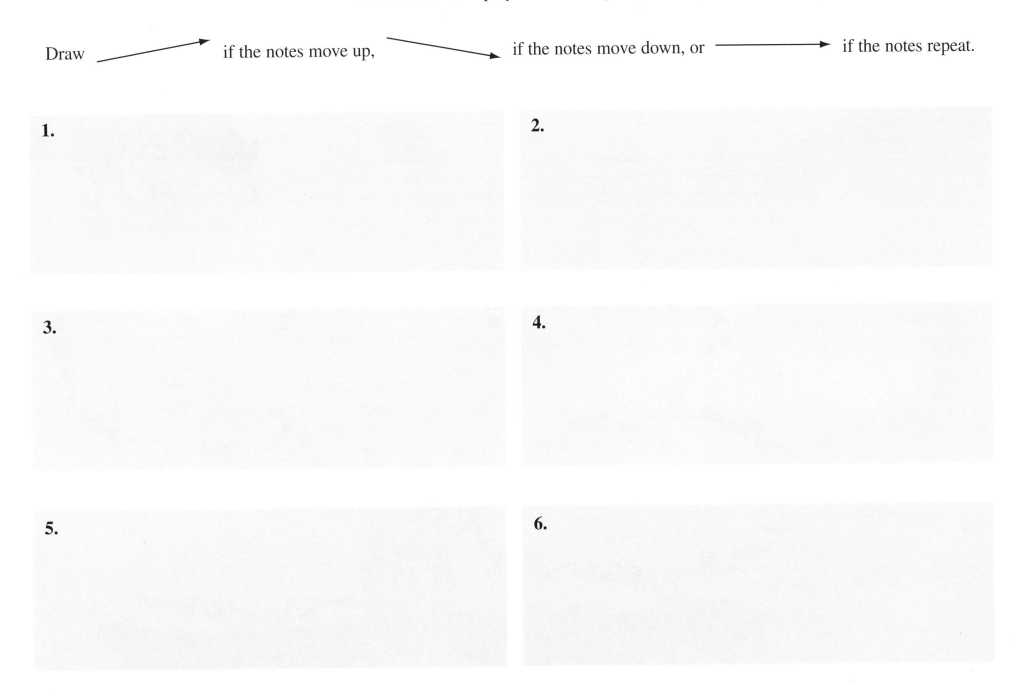

1.

2.

3.

4.

5.

6.

Teacher's Examples on pg. 48

Use with Lesson Book 1, pg. 37

The Bass Clef
(F Clef)

Bass clefs are easy to make. Just follow Bear's instructions.
Trace each step and then draw your own Bass Clef.

1.   **2.**   **3.**

This is the F line. Colour it blue.

1. Colour each F line blue.
2. Draw a Bass Clef on each staff.
3. Draw the note F on each staff.

Notes on the Bass Staff

Spike is hiding.
Follow the maze to find him!

**Either name or write
the notes as you find them.**

Use with Lesson Book 1, pg. 39

Treble Clef Sign
(G Clef)

If you follow Bear's instructions, you will make a Treble Clef.
Trace each step as you then draw your own.

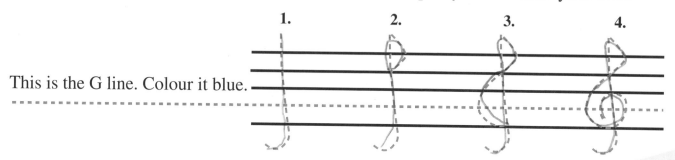

This is the G line. Colour it blue.

1. Colour each G line blue.
2. Draw a Treble Clef on each staff.
3. Draw the note G on each staff.

Notes on the Treble Staff

It's time for a game of hopscotch!

Either name or write the notes in each square.

Use with Lesson Book 1, pg. 41

The Grand Staff – A Musical Map

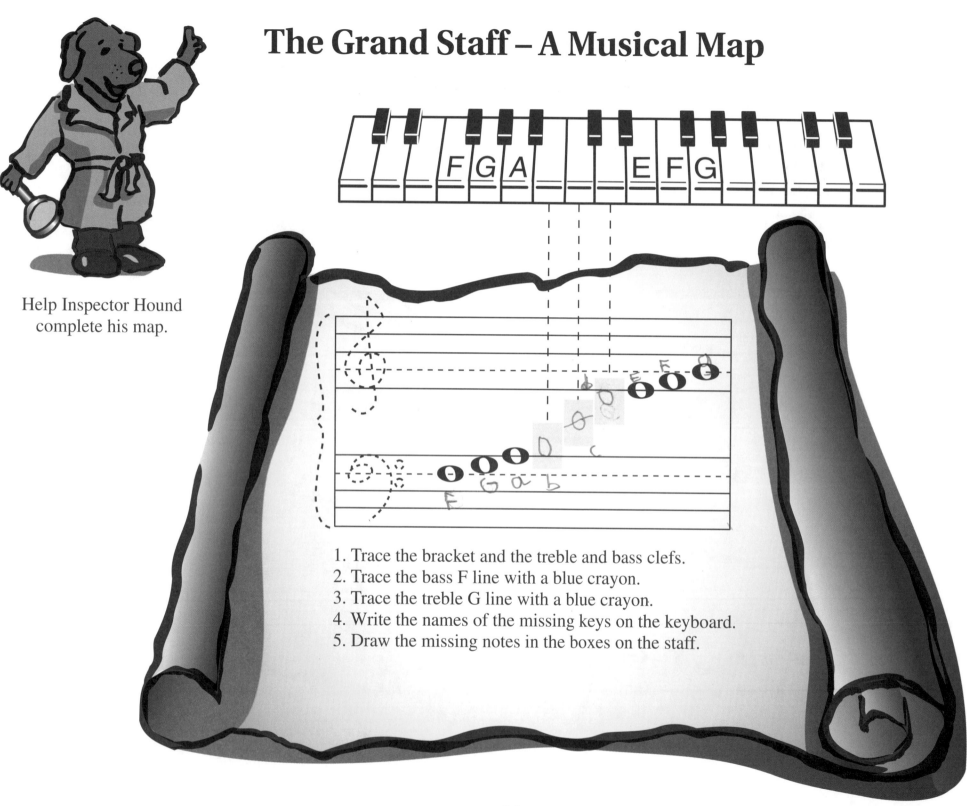

Help Inspector Hound complete his map.

1. Trace the bracket and the treble and bass clefs.
2. Trace the bass F line with a blue crayon.
3. Trace the treble G line with a blue crayon.
4. Write the names of the missing keys on the keyboard.
5. Draw the missing notes in the boxes on the staff.

Notes Above and Below Middle C

Complete the stepping pattern for *Tambourine Tune*,
one of Party Cat's favorite melodies.

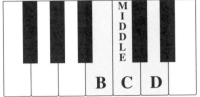

1. Draw the missing crotchet notes in the boxes.
2. In the second line, write the name of each note with a line above or below it.
3. Play the completed melody.

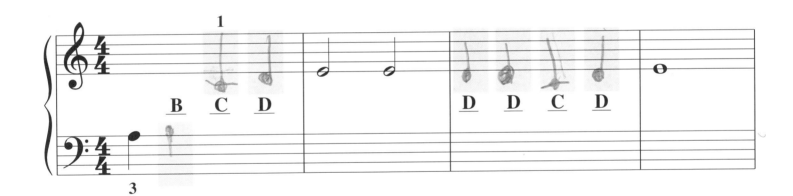

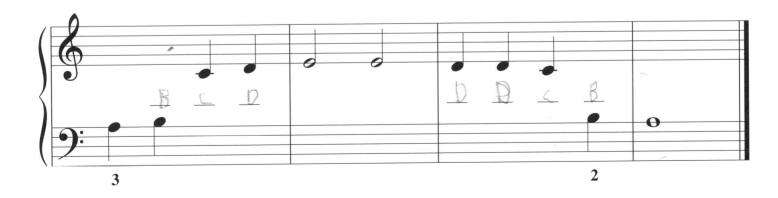

Use with Lesson Book 1, pg. 44

The Grand Staff Garden

Two inchworms found a surprise in the *Grand Staff Garden*.
Discover their names and what they found by completing the sentence below.

Write the name of each note in its blank in the sentence below.

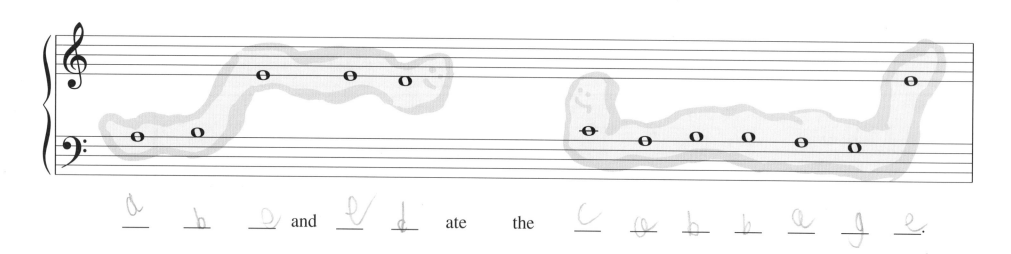

_a_ _b_ _b_ and _e_ _d_ ate the _c a b b a g e_.

From *Soft* to LOUD

Listen as your teacher plays *Tambourine Tune* two different times.
Circle the sign that matches the sound of the music each time you hear it.

| 1. | *f* | *mp* |

| 2. | *mf* | *p* |

Arrange the dynamic signs above from soft to loud in the boxes below.

Now arrange the signs from loud to soft.

Teacher's Examples on pg. 48

Use with Lesson Book 1, pg. 46

Skips
(3rds)

Match each skip on the staff to the same skip on the
keyboard by drawing a line from Column A to Column B.

A

B

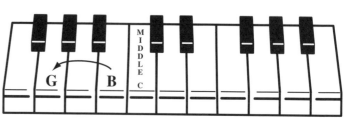

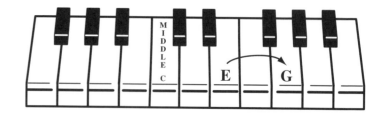

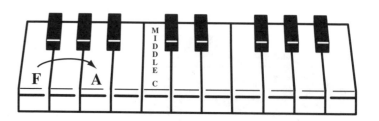

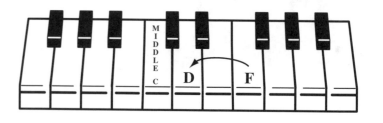

Steps, Skips, and Repeated Notes

Study each example. Do the notes move by step, skip or repeat?

1. Underline the correct answer.

2. Listen as your teacher plays one pattern from each box.
   Circle the example you hear.

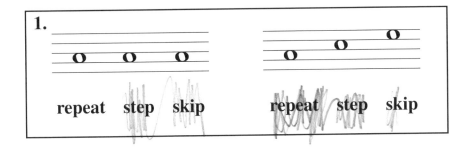

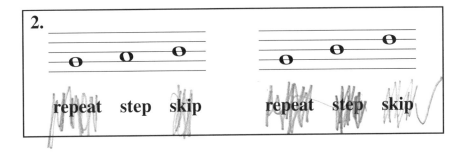

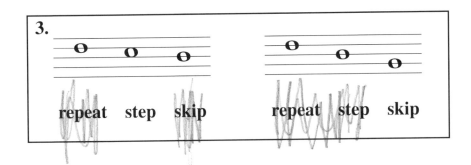

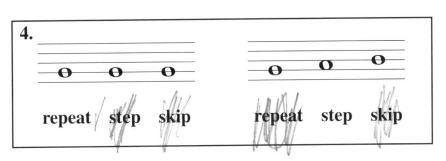

STEP

REPEAT

SKIP

Teacher's Examples on pg. 48

Use with Lesson Book 1, pg. 51

More Steps

Fill each of Party Cat's balloons with three semibreve notes that **step** higher or lower.
Use the arrows as a guide.

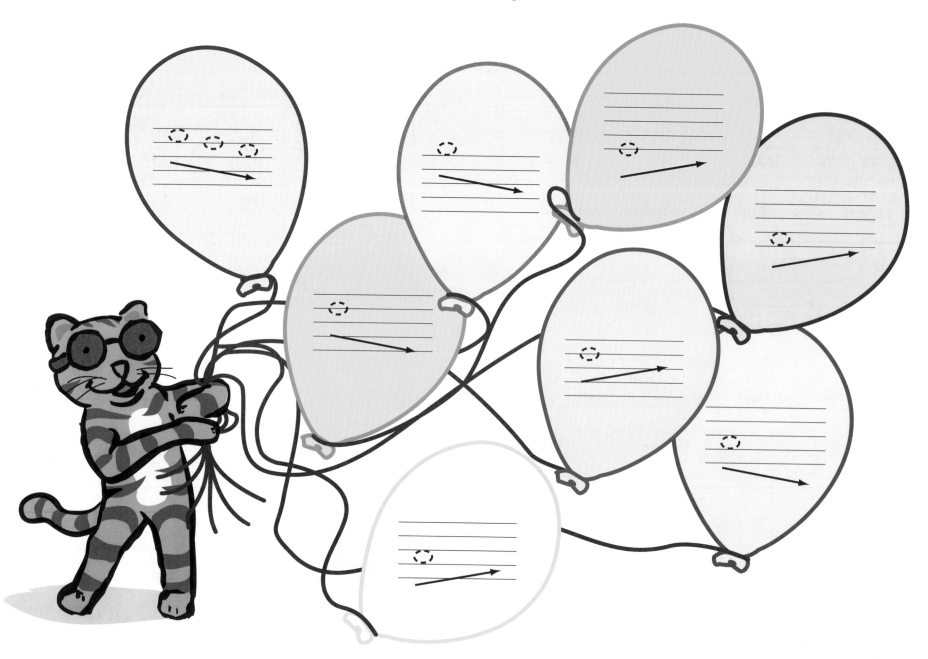

More Skips

Fill each of Spike's balloons with three
semibreve notes that **skip** higher or lower.
Use the arrows as a guide.

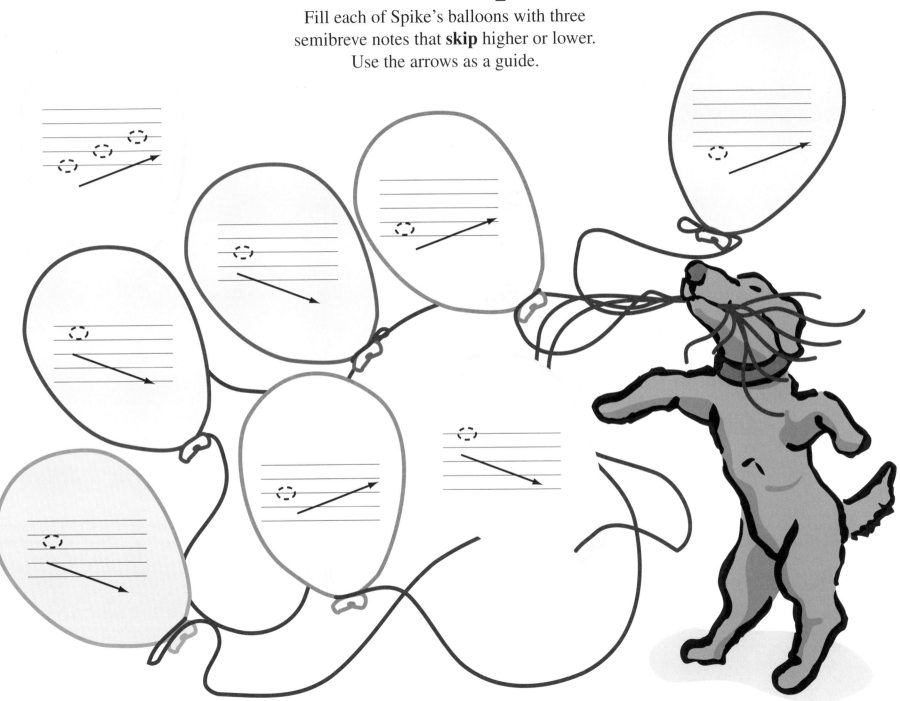

Up to Tempo!

Tempo marks tell the mood of the music and the speed of the piece.

Circle the picture that describes the tempo marking.

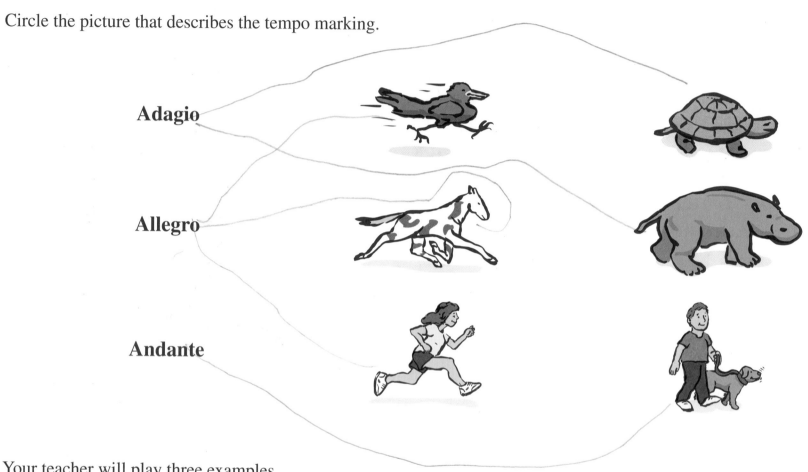

Adagio

Allegro

Andante

Your teacher will play three examples.
Circle the tempo mark that fits the speed and mood of the music.

1.
Adagio

Andante

Allegro

2.
Adagio

Andante

Allegro

3.
Adagio

Andante

Allegro

Teacher's Examples on pg. 48

Use with Lesson Book 1, pg. 55

The Dotted Minim Note

A dotted minim note equals 3 beats.

Play the first two bars of *Camptown Races (Trumpet Man)*.

Your teacher will complete the first line of the song by playing one of the examples below.
Circle the example your teacher plays.

1.

2.

3.

Now play the first four bars of *Camptown Races*.

Teacher's Examples on pg. 48

Use with Lesson Book 1, pg. 58

3/4 or 4/4 ?

Bear wrote down some of his favourite songs,
but he forgot the time signatures.

1. Write the correct time signature in the box at the beginning of each piece.
2. Play each melody.

Pop, Goes The Weasel

Surprise Symphony

Home, Home On The Range

Yankee Doodle

Rhythm Jam

Party Cat is practicing for his next piano lesson.
Help him count the rhythm in his new pieces.

1. Circle the note or rest in the blue box that will complete the
   rhythm in each bar.
2. Clap and count each example.

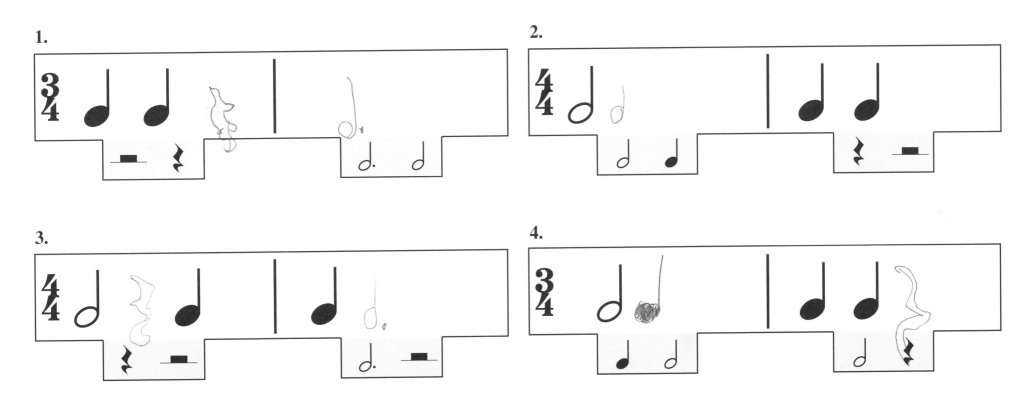

Use with Lesson Book 1, pg. 60

All Tied Up

The conductor surprised the orchestra by changing the
melody to Haydn's "Surprise" Symphony. Help him with his joke.

1. Play the melody as written.
2. Add a tie to all the repeated notes.
3. Play the new melody holding each tied note.

4. Play the melody below.

(circle one)

Does this melody sound: **the same as**   or   **different than**   the melody with ties above?

Relay Review

Spike and Party Cat are racing to finish their theory workbook.
Match the correct answers by drawing a line from Column A to Column B.
Record your time in the box at the end of each race.

START

A	B
(notes on staff)	moderately soft
mp	crotchet rest = 1 beat
(notes on staff)	repeated notes
4/4	Four beats fill every bar. ♩ gets one beat.
♩	minim note = 2 beats
f	steps (2nds)
(rest)	loud
♩	crotchet note = 1 beat

FINISH   Seconds

START

A	B
(notes on staff)	soft
(rest)	tie
(whole note)	moderately loud
p	three beats fill every bar. ♩ gets one beat.
♩.	dotted minim note = 3 beats
mf	semibreve note = 4 beats
3/4	minim rest = 2 beats
(notes on staff)	skips (3rds)

FINISH   Seconds

The winner is:
_____

47

Use with Lesson Book 1, pg. 64

Teacher's Examples

Page 3 (Play)

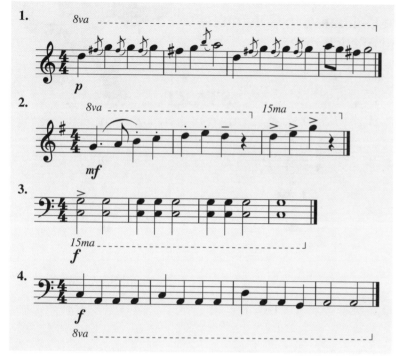

Page 12 (Clap)

Page 29 (Play)

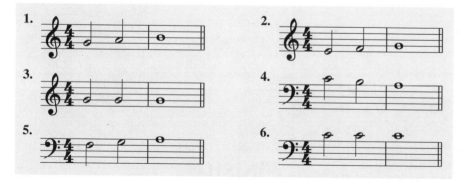

Page 37 (Play)

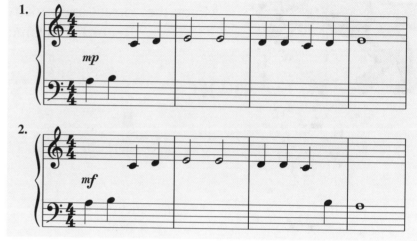

Page 39 (Play)

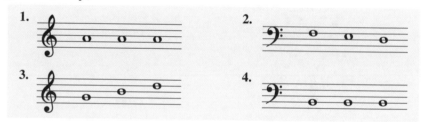

Page 42 (Play)

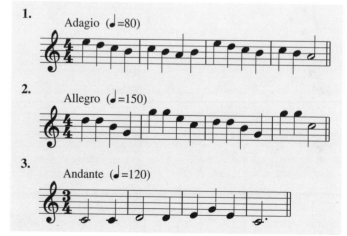

Page 43 (Play)